KU-350-176

This book belongs to

. . . .

Can I play with a monster?

by Mary Atkinson

make
believe
ideas

Get the most from this reader

Before reading:

- Look at the pictures and discuss them together. Ask questions such as, "What colour is this monster?"

- Relate the topic to your child's world. For example, say: "Who do you like to play with? Why?"

- Familiarise your child with book vocabulary by using terms such as *word*, *letter*, *title*, *author* and *text*.

During reading:

- Prompt your child to sound out unknown words. Draw attention to neglected middle or end sounds.

- Encourage your child to use the pictures as clues to unknown words.

- Occasionally ask what might happen next, and then check together as you read on.

- Monitor your child's understanding. Repeated readings can improve fluency and comprehension.

- Keep reading sessions short and enjoyable. Stop if your child becomes tired or frustrated.

After reading:

- Discuss the book. Encourage your child to form opinions with questions such as, "What did you like best about this book?"

- Help your child work through the fun activities at the back of the book. Then ask him or her to reread the story. Praise any improvement.

Hello, red monster!
Would you like to
play cars with me?

Yes, it would be fun
to play cars with you.

Hello, pink monster!
Would you like to
twirl yo-yos with me?

Yes, it would be fun to twirl yo-yos with you.

Yes, it would be fun
to play ball with you.

Yes, it would be fun to make music with you.

Hello, yellow monster!
Would you like to
draw pictures with me?

16

Yes, it would be fun to draw pictures with you.

Yes, it would be fun to skateboard with you.

Hello, orange monster! Would you like to eat cupcakes with me?

No, all the cupcakes are for me!

Discussion Questions

1 What colour monster rides a skateboard?

2 Why couldn't the boy eat any cupcakes?

3 Which monster is your favourite? Why?

✤ Sight Words ✤

Learning sight words helps you read fluently. Practise these sight words from the book. Use them in sentences of your own.

would

for

play

like

with

me

on

all

❧ Rhyming Words ❧

Can you find the rhyming pairs?
Say them aloud.

bake

way

play

make

red

bed

ball

clue

meat

eat

blue

fall

Writing Practice

Read the words, and then trace them with your finger.

draw

like

green

music

hello

yellow

❧ Silly Sentences ❧

Have fun filling in the gap in each sentence. Use the ideas below or make up your own.

Would you like to .... ?

It would be fun to .... with you .